Theatre Songs *for*

Theatre Songs *for* Singers

Hal Leonard Europe
Distributed by Music Sales

Exclusive Distributors:
Music Sales Limited
8/9 Frith Street, London W1D 3JB, England.
Music Sales Pty Limited
120 Rothschild Avenue, Rosebery, NSW 2018, Australia.

Order No. HLE90000869
ISBN 0-7119-8258-9
This book © Copyright 2000 by Hal Leonard Europe

Compiled and edited by Richard Walters
Cover design by Chloë Alexander
Printed in the USA

Your Guarantee of Quality
As publishers, we strive to produce every book to the highest
commercial standards.
The book has been carefully designed to minimise awkward page turns
and to make playing from it a real pleasure.
Throughout, the printing and binding have been planned to ensure
a sturdy, attractive publication which should give years of enjoyment.
If your copy fails to meet our high standards, please inform us and
we will gladly replace it.

Music Sales' complete catalogue describes thousands of titles and is
available in full colour sections by subject, direct from Music Sales
Limited. Please state your areas of interest and send a cheque/postal
order for £1.50 for postage to: Music Sales Limited, Newmarket Road,
Bury St. Edmunds, Suffolk IP33 3YB, England.

www.musicsales.com

Notes On The Shows 4

BEAUTY AND THE BEAST
Gaston 12
If I Can't Love Her 20

CAROUSEL
If I Loved You 28
Soliloquy 32

CINDERELLA
Do I Love You Because You're Beautiful 64

COMPANY
Marry Me A Little 52
Sorry-Grateful 47

FOLLIES
The Road You Didn't Take 66

GENTLEMEN PREFER BLONDES
Bye Bye Baby 89

GUYS AND DOLLS
Luck Be A Lady 76 ✓
More I Cannot Wish You 86
My Time Of Day 74

JESUS CHRIST SUPERSTAR
Pilate's Dream 92 ✓

LES MISÉRABLES
Empty Chairs At Empty Tables 124
Stars 119 ✓

THE LITTLE MERMAID (film)
Les Poissons 95

MAN OF LA MANCHA
Dulcinea 100
The Impossible Dream 104
The Man Of La Mancha (I, Don Quixote) 108

MARTIN GUERRE
Justice Will Be Done 114

ME AND MY GIRL
Leaning On A Lamp-Post 128

THE MOST HAPPY FELLA
Joey, Joey, Joey 134

NINE
Guido's Song 141

OKLAHOMA!
Lonely Room 150
Oh, What A Beautiful Mornin' 155 ✓
The Surrey With The Fringe On Top 162

ON THE TOWN
Lonely Town 178

PARADE
It's Hard To Speak My Heart 173

SHE LOVES ME
Ilona 184

SHOW BOAT
Ol' Man River 190 ✓

SIDE SHOW
You Should Be Loved 197

SOUTH PACIFIC
Some Enchanted Evening 202 ✓
This Nearly Was Mine 206

SUNSET BOULEVARD
The Greatest Star Of All 211

THE UNSINKABLE MOLLY BROWN
I'll Never Say No 216

BEAUTY AND THE BEAST

MUSIC: Alan Menken
LYRICS: Howard Ashman and Tim Rice
BOOK: Linda Woolverton
OPENED: 18/4/94, New York; 1999, London

Disney made its Broadway debut with a big-budget adaptation of its own Oscar-nominated animated film musical. Like the classic fairy tale on which it is based, *Beauty and the Beast* tells the story of a witch who transforms a haughty prince into a fearsome Beast (and his retainers into household objects). Her spell can be broken only when the prince learns how to love, and how to inspire love. Lyricist Ashman died in 1991 just as the film was coming out. The stage score includes several trunk songs written for the film, but not used, plus five new songs with lyrics by Broadway veteran Rice. In a nearby village, headstrong heroine Belle finds herself beset by the town stud Gaston, who believes he's God's gift to womanhood. Belle rejects him anyway, and it's up to Gaston's drinking buddies to comfort him with the comic ego massage, "Gaston." Is there any wonder the Beast starts to look pretty good to her, even after he takes her prisoner in his enchanted castle? Belle soon finds herself adopted by the various living clocks, teapots, candlesticks and cutlery who strive to matchmake their beastly boss and the eligible but understandably resistant maiden. The Beast can't help his insensitivity toward Belle, but he knows she's his last chance for humanity—in several senses—as he sings in his soliloquy "If I Can't Love Her."

CAROUSEL

MUSIC: Richard Rodgers
LYRICS AND BOOK: Oscar Hammerstein II
OPENED: 19/4/45, New York; 7/6/50, London

The collaborators of *Oklahoma!* chose Ferenc Molnar's *Liliom* as the basis for their second show. Oscar Hammerstein shifted Molnar's Budapest locale to a late 19th century fishing village in New England. The two principal roles are Billy Bigelow, a shiftless carnival barker, and Julie Jordan, an ordinary factory worker. This is not merely a simple boy meets girl plot, but contains a predominant theme of tragedy throughout most of the play. The score is rich with musical high points, the first coming with "If I Loved You," sung by Julie and Billy at their first meeting. Billy's famous "Soliloquy" is Richard Rodgers longest and most operatic song, and can truly be considered an aria.

CINDERELLA

MUSIC: Richard Rodgers
LYRICS AND BOOK: Oscar Hammerstein II
FIRST AIRED: 31/3/57 on CBS-TV (USA)

Ever the innovators, Rodgers and Hammerstein were among the first to explore the new medium of television with a full-length original TV musical. The original broadcast also was fortunate in securing the services of Julie Andrews, fresh from her triumph as the Cinderella-like heroine of *My Fair Lady*. In adapting the children's fairy tale, Hammerstein was careful not to alter or update the familiar story about a young woman who collaborates with her Fairy Godmother to overcome the plots of her evil stepmother and stepsisters so she can go to an opulent ball and meet a handsome prince. Cinderella still loses her magical glass slipper, and the Prince proclaims that he will marry the girl whose foot fits the slipper. Because the original production was filmed live and could not be preserved except in black-and-white kinescope, a new production was captured on tape in 1965. A stage adaptation toured the U.S., and the musical finally made its New York stage debut in 1993 at New York City Opera. An opulent new version was made for television in 1998, with pop singer Brandy in the title role and Bernadette Peters as the stepmother. The young prince sings "Do I Love You Because You're Beautiful" to Cinderella after their love-at-first-sight moment at the ball.

COMPANY

MUSIC AND LYRICS: Stephen Sondheim
BOOK: George Furth
OPENED: 26/4/70, New York; 8/1/72, London

Company was the first of the Sondheim musicals to have been directed by Harold Prince, and more than any other musical, reflects America in the 1970s. The show is a plotless evening about five affluent couples living in a Manhattan apartment building, and their excessively protective feelings about a charming, but somewhat indifferent bachelor named Bobby. They want to fix him up and see him married, even though it's clear their own marriages are far from perfect. In the end he seems ready to take the plunge. The songs are often very sophisticated, expressing the ambivalent or caustic attitudes of fashionable New Yorkers of the time. Making a connection with another person, the show seems to say, is the key to happiness. Bobby's fear of commitment is obvious in "Marry Me a Little," in which he pleads for a relationship that goes only so deep and no deeper. The number was cut from the original production but restored as an Act I finale in the 1995 Broadway revival. An Off-Broadway revue of Sondheim songs also borrowed the song title as its overall title. "Sorry-Grateful" expresses the often ambivalent attitude about marriage.

FOLLIES

MUSIC AND LYRICS: Stephen Sondheim
BOOK: James Goldman
OPENED: 4/4/71, New York; 21/7/87, London

Taking place at a reunion of former Ziegfeld Follies-type showgirls, the musical deals with the reality of life as contrasted with the unreality of the theatre. *Follies* explores this theme through the lives of two couples, the upper-class, unhappy, Phyllis and Benjamin Stone, and the middle-class, also unhappy, Sally and Buddy Plummer. *Follies* also shows us these four as they were in their pre-marital youth. The young actors appear as ghosts to haunt their elder selves. Because the show is about the past, and often in flashback, Sondheim styled his songs to evoke some of the theatre's great composers and lyricists of the past, with a cast that suggests some of the vivid personalities of 1920s Broadway. "The Road You Didn't Take" is Ben's mid-life crisis song. (It was replaced by "Make the Most of Your Music" for the 1987 London production.

GENTLEMEN PREFER BLONDES

MUSIC: Jule Styne
LYRICS: Leo Robin
BOOK: Joseph Stein and Anita Loos
OPENED: 8/12/49, New York; 20/8/62, London

Based on Anita Loos' popular 1926 novel and play of the same name, *Gentlemen Prefer Blondes* took a satirical look at the wacky, gold-digging world of 1920s flappers. Playing Lorelei Lee, the husband-hunting "Little Girl from Little Rock," Carol Channing scored a star-making success in her first major role. The show's action takes place mostly aboard the liner *Ile de France*, which is taking Lorelei and her chum Dorothy Paris, courtesy of Lorelei's generous friend, button tycoon Gus Esmond. En route, the girls meet a number of accommodating gentlemen, and romantic complications ensue. A 1953 film version (minus much of the score) starred Marilyn Monroe and Jane Russell. A new Broadway version in 1973 extensively changed the score, and was retitled *Lorelei*.

6

GUYS AND DOLLS

MUSIC AND LYRICS: Frank Loesser
BOOK: Abe Burrows and Jo Swerling
OPENED: 24/11/50, New York; 28/5/53, London

Populated by the hard-shelled but soft-centered characters who inhabit the world of writer Damon Runyon, this "Musical Fable of Broadway" tells the tale of how Miss Sarah Brown of the Save-a-Soul Mission saves the souls of assorted Times Square riff-raff while losing her heart to the smooth-talking gambler, Sky Masterson. A more comic romance involves Nathan Detroit, who runs the "oldest established permanent floating crap game in New York," and Miss Adelaide, the star of the Hot Box nightclub, to whom he has been engaged for fourteen years. The gambler Sky sings "My Time of Day" in the dark hours just before dawn to Sarah, his unlikely girlfriend from the Salvation Army. In "Luck Be a Lady Tonight" Sky has bet on a roll of the dice that if he wins, the losers will pay him not in money, but with their souls—they'll have to show up at the mission prayer meeting, which keeps the mission open and Sarah happy and in the neighborhood. "More I Cannot Wish You" is sung as a song of blessing by Arvide, Sarah's paternal fellow mission worker, to her about following her heart and loving Sky. An enormously successful revival opened on Broadway in 1992. The 1955 film version stars Frank Sinatra, Marlon Brando, Jean Simmons and Vivian Blaine.

JESUS CHRIST SUPERSTAR

MUSIC: Andrew Lloyd Webber
LYRICS: Tim Rice
OPENED: 12/10/71, New York; 9/8/72, London

This was the show that boosted Andrew Lloyd Webber and Tim Rice to international prominence, a musical that presumed to make a Broadway musical star out of Jesus and to make the last weeks of his life sing and dance. Though *Superstar* was conceived as a theatre piece, Lloyd Webber and Rice couldn't convince producers that their "rock opera" had the slightest chance. Instead, they recorded it as a rock album, and it immediately became a smash hit, the first such "concept album" of a show in development. Concert tours of the show followed, and soon producers didn't need any more convincing that this would fly in the theatre. Despite some mixed press about the production, and some outcries and picketing from religious groups, the piece had its appeal, particularly among the young. The show broke all records in London, and pioneered the concept of a "through-sung" opera-like musical, which had its effect on shows to follow, including *Evita, Cats, Les Misérables, Miss Saigon* and *The Phantom of the Opera*. A 1974 film followed. A Broadway revival opened in the year 2000.

LES MISÉRABLES

MUSIC: Claude-Michel Schönberg
LYRICS: Herbert Kretzmer and Alain Boublil
ORIGINAL FRENCH TEXT: Alain Boublil and Jean-Marc Natel
DIRECTORS: Trevor Nunn and John Caird
CHOREOGRAPHER: Kate Flatt
OPENED: 9/80, Paris; 4/12/85, London; 12/3/87, New York

This quasi-operatic pop epic was one of the defining musicals of the 1980s, distilling the drama from the 1,200 page Victor Hugo novel of social injustice and the plight of the downtrodden (the "miserable ones" of the title). The original Parisian version contained only a few songs; many more were added when the show opened in London. Thus, most of the show's songs were originally written in English. The plot is too rich to encapsulate, but centers on Jean Valjean, a prisoner sentenced to years of hard labor for stealing a loaf of bread for his starving family. He escapes and tries to start a new life, but soon finds himself pursued by the relentless policeman Javert. The pursuit continues for years, across a tapestry of early 19th century France that includes an armed uprising against the government, in which Valjean takes a heroic part. Along the way he acquires an adopted daughter, Cosette, who grows into womanhood and attracts the attention of the handsome revolutionary Marius, and the enmity of a rival, Eponine. "Empty Chairs at Empty Tables" is sung by Marius after most of his companions are killed in the student uprisings of 1832 in Paris. "Stars" is Javert's song of determined pursuit of Valjean.

THE LITTLE MERMAID
(film)

MUSIC: Alan Menken
LYRICS: Howard Ashman
RELEASED: 1989, Walt Disney

Based on the Hans Christian Andersen tale, *The Little Mermaid* marked the Disney studio's triumphant return to the animated screen musical. Ariel, a young, sea-dwelling mermaid, longs to be human. She falls in love with the human prince and, aided by some magic, gets her wish. The phenomonal artistic and commercial success of this film spawned a renaissance of big-budget feature films made for children. Besides the theatrical income and merchandising, *The Little Mermaid* and its Disney successors have gone on to become the bestselling videocassettes in history. "Les Poissons" is the palace chef's bright waltz in honor of his favorite dish, not something to be taken lightly when half the cast of the movie is of that variety.

MAN OF LA MANCHA

MUSIC: Mitch Leigh
LYRICS: Joe Darion
BOOK: Dale Wasserman
OPENED: 22/11/65, New York; 24/4/68, London

Cervantes' great demented hero, Don Quixote, is the unlikely hero of this very popular musical of the '60s. Although very much rooted in the Spanish novelist's work, this musical version was adapted from Dale Wasserman's television play, *I, Don Quixote*. The principal characters, besides Don Quixote, are Sancho Panza, the Don's squire and sidekick, and Aldonza, who Quixote sees as his grand lady, Dulcinea. Richard Kiley was the original New York Don, certainly one of the best baritone roles in musical theatre literature.

MARTIN GUERRE

MUSIC: Claude-Michel Schönberg
BOOK: Alain Boublil and Claude-Michel Schönberg
LYRICS: Alain Boublil and Stephen Clark
OPENED: 6/96, London

There have been several major revisions of the Boublil/Schönberg musical since its inception in 1991. Besides the musical, the 16th century legend inspired the books *The Wife of Martin Guerre* by Janet Lewis, and *The Return of Martin Guerre* by Natalie Zemon Davis. The 1982 film *The Return of Martin Guerre*, starring Gerard Depardieu, is based on the Davis novel. In 1560 the French Catholic mercenary Martin Guerre tells his friend, Arnaud du Thil, of his childhood in the village of Artigat, and of his arranged marriage to Bertrande du Rols. The villainous Guillaume, rebuffed by Bertrande, had convinced the superstitious villagers that Martin's failure to conceive an heir brought on their crop failures. Martin was exiled, later to join the mercenary corps. Martin is stabbed while saving Arnaud's life. Arnaud escapes and goes to Artigat, where he is mysteriously believed to be Martin Guerre returning after seven years. Bertrande falls in love with Arnaud, even though she knows he is not Martin. Guillaume, still hoping for Bertrande, charges Arnaud with fraud for impersonating Martin Guerre. Guillaume incites vengeful violence in the townspeople when the judge fails to condemn Arnaud ("Justice Will Be Done"). At a dramatic moment the real Martin Guerre returns and denounces Arnaud. Learning of the true love between Bertrande and Arnaud, in the spirit of friendship Martin decides to let them go. Protecting Martin from Guillaume's knife, Arnaud is stabbed and dies.

ME AND MY GIRL

MUSIC: Noel Gay
LYRICS: Various
BOOK: L. Arthur Rose and Douglas Furber, revised by Stephen Fry
OPENED: 1937, London;
New production: 1985, London; 1986, New York

The cockney character of Bill Snibson originated in 1935 in *Twenty to One*, played by comedian Lupino Lane. The actor became so attached to the role that he initiated a new musical show built around Bill two years later, resulting in *Me and My Girl*, a light social-class song and dance show in which Bill finds himself heir to an aristocratic title. Comedy results from the friction between the proletarian Bill and his hoity-toity new relations. Bill also has to decide whether to submit to an arranged match with a snobby blueblood, or stay true to his special gal from back in Lambeth. Revivals came to London in 1941, 1945 and 1949, but the major rediscovery of the show came in 1985 when Robert Lindsay reinvented the role in London, then in New York.

THE MOST HAPPY FELLA

MUSIC, LYRICS AND BOOK: Frank Loesser
OPENED: 3/5/56, New York; 21/4/60, London

Adapted from Sidney Howard's Pulitzer Prize-winning play, *They Knew What They Wanted*, Loesser's musical was a particularly ambitious work for the Broadway theatre, with more than thirty separate musical numbers, including arias, duets, trios, quartets, choral pieces, and recitatives. Robust, emotional expressions were interspersed with more traditional specialty numbers, though in the manner of an opera; the program credits did not list individual selections. In the story, set in California's Napa Valley, an aging vineyard owner proposes by mail to a waitress he calls Rosabella. She accepts, but is so upset to find Tony old and fat that on their wedding night she allows herself to be seduced by Joe, the handsome ranch foreman. After some time, Rosabella learns to love Tony, however, she soon realizes Tony treats her not as an equal, but as a child. Once Tony discovers that Rosabella is to have another man's child, he threatens to kill Joe, but there is a reconciliation and the vintner offers to raise the child as his own. A 1979 Broadway revival, starring Giorgio Tozzi, ran for 52 performances. A more successful revival ran in New York in 1991-2, resulting in a new recording of the score. "Joey, Joey, Joey" is the farmhand Joe's song about his restlessness to move on.

NINE

MUSIC AND LYRICS: Maury Yeston
BOOK: Arthur Kopit and Mario Fratti
OPENED: 9/5/82, New York

The influence of the director-choreographer was emphasized again with Tommy Tune's highly stylized, visually striking production of *Nine*, which, besides being a feast for the eyes is also one of the very few non-Sondheim Broadway scores to have true musical substance and merit from the 1970s and 1980s. The musical evolved from Yeston's fascination with Federico Fellini's semi-autobiographical 1963 film *8 1/2*. The story spotlights Guido Contini (played originally by Raul Julia), a celebrated but tormented director who has come to a Venetian spa for a rest, and his relationships with his wife, his mistress, his protégée, his producer and his mother. The production, which flashes back to Guido's youth and also takes place in his imagination, offers such inventive touches as an overture in which Guido conducts his women as if they were instruments, and an impressionistic version of the Folies Bergères. "Guido's Song" is the main character's boisterous entrance number.

OKLAHOMA!

MUSIC: Richard Rodgers
LYRICS AND BOOK: Oscar Hammerstein II
OPENED: 31/3/43, New York; 29/4/47, London

There are many reasons why *Oklahoma!* is a recognized landmark in the history of the musical theatre. In the initial collaboration between Richard Rodgers and Oscar Hammerstein II, it not only expertly fused the major elements in the production—story, songs and dances—it also utilized dream ballets to reveal hidden desires and fears of the principals. In addition, the musical, based on Lynn Riggs' play, *Green Grow the Lilacs*, was the first with a book that honestly depicted the kind of rugged pioneers who had once tilled the land and tended the cattle. Set in Indian Territory soon after the turn of the century, *Oklahoma!* spins a simple tale mostly concerned with whether the decent Curly or the menacing Jud gets to take Laurey to the box social. Though she chooses Jud in a fit of pique, Laurey really loves Curly and they soon make plans to marry. At their wedding they join in celebrating Oklahoma's impending statehood, then—after Jud is accidentally killed in a fight with Curly—the couple ride off in their surrey with the fringe on top. With its Broadway run of five years, nine months, *Oklahoma!* established a long-run record that it held for fifteen years. It also toured the United States and Canada for over a decade. Various revivals have played in New York and London. "Oh, What a Beautiful Mornin'" is Curly's bucolic ode that opens the show. The mean guy outcast Jud sings angrily and poignantly about his life in "Lonely Room."

ON THE TOWN

MUSIC: Leonard Bernstein
LYRICS AND BOOK: Betty Comden and Adolph Green
OPENED: 28/12/44, New York; 30/5/63, London

This major show was the Broadway debut of some very major talents: composer Leonard Bernstein, choreographer Jerome Robbins, and writers Betty Comden and Adolph Green. It was based on the Robbins-Bernstein ballet from the previous year, *Fancy Free*. The story is of three sailors on a 24-hour leave in New York City. The musical was revived Off-Broadway in 1959 and in 1971 on Broadway. The movie version was released in 1949 and stars Gene Kelly, Frank Sinatra, Vera-Ellen and Betty Garrett. A new complete recording of the show has also been made in recent years. Gabey's "Lonely Town" is a lyrical expression of a sailor who arrives in crowded New York without knowing a soul there.

PARADE

MUSIC AND LYRICS: Jason Robert Brown
BOOK: Alfred Uhry
OPENED: 17/12/98, New York

The musical that opened at New York's Lincoln Center got mostly negative reviews for its relentlessly downbeat subject matter: the true story of Leo Frank, a Jewish factory manager accused of—and lynched for—the murder of Mary Phagan, an underage female worker, in 1913 Atlanta. But the sterling cast album released a few months later helped build a cult of devoted fans and the show went on to win the 1999 Tony Awards for Best Score and Best Book of a Musical. Leo, at his lawyer's urging, takes the stand to speak in his own defense. "It's Hard to Speak My Heart" reveals his true feelings, insisting, to the song's heartbeat rhythm, "I never touched that child."

SHE LOVES ME

MUSIC: Jerry Bock
LYRICS: Sheldon Harnick
BOOK: Joe Masteroff
OPENED: 23/4/63, New York

The closely integrated, melody drenched score of *She Loves Me* is certainly one of the best ever written for a musical comedy. It was based on a Hungarian play, *Parfumerie*, by Miklos Laszlo, that had already been used as the basis for two films, *The Shop Around the Corner* and *In the Good Old Summertime* (with the setting changed to America). Set in the 1930s in Budapest, the tale is of the people who work in Maraczek's Parfumerie, principally the constantly squabbling sales clerk Amalia Balash and the manager Georg Nowack. It is soon revealed that they are anonymous pen pals who agree to meet one night at the Café Imperiale, though neither knows the other's identity. Georg realizes that it is Amalia who is waiting for him in the restaurant, but doesn't let on, leaving her to sit there for hours. After she calls in sick their relationship blossoms into love when Georg brings her ice cream; eventually, he is emboldened to reveal his identity by quoting from one of Amalia's letters. Kodaly, the skirt-chasing employee at the parfumerie, is smitten with a fellow female clerk, "Ilona," at least temporarily. The show was revived in New York in 1993.

SHOW BOAT

MUSIC: Jerome Kern
LYRICS AND BOOK: Oscar Hammerstein II
OPENED: 27/12/27, New York; 3/5/28, London

No show ever to hit Broadway was more historically important, and at the same time more beloved, than *Show Boat*, that landmark of the 1927 season. Edna Ferber's novel of life on the Mississippi was the source for this musical/operetta, and provided a rich plot and characters which Kern and Hammerstein amplified to become some of the most memorable ever to grace the stage. *Show Boat* is not only a summing up of all that had come before it, both in the musical and operetta genres, but plants a seed of complete congruity which later further blossoms in the more adventurous shows of the '30s, '40s, and '50s. Almost every song in the show is a familiar gem: "Make Believe"; "Can't Help Lovin' Dat Man"; "You Are Love"; "Why Do I Love You?"; "Bill"; and that most classic song of the musical stage, "Ol' Man River." The last is Joe's philosophical song of perspective on his hard life. A major revival opened on Broadway in 1994.

SIDE SHOW

MUSIC: Henry Krieger
LYRICS AND BOOK: Bill Russell
OPENED: 16/10/97, New York

She's Daisy; she's Violet. They're Siamese twins. That's the offbeat story of this fictionalized biography of real-life conjoined twins Daisy and Violet Hilton, who climb from carnival freak show through vaudeville to the Ziegfeld Follies in the early decades of the 20th century. The musical concentrates on their doomed romance with two men, Terry and Buddy, who act as their coach and agent, but who ultimately can't get over what they see as the sisters' deformity. The show attracted a small but devoted cult that was unable to keep the show running more than three months. Terry and Buddy pluck the sisters out of the clutches of the sadistic freak show manager, Terry finds the only way he can allow his feelings of love to blossom is when he imagines the conjoined sisters as whole, separated women. When Jake finds that the sisters' love is going unrequited, he reveals his own hitherto hidden feelings, in "You Should Be Loved."

SOUTH PACIFIC

MUSIC: Richard Rodgers
LYRICS: Oscar Hammerstein II
OPENED: 7/4/49, New York; 1/11/51, London

South Pacific had the second longest Broadway run of the nine musicals with songs by Richard Rodgers and Oscar Hammerstein II. Director Joshua Logan first urged the partners to adapt a short story, "Fo' Dolla," contained in James Michener's book about World War II, *Tales of the South Pacific*. Rodgers and Hammerstein, however, felt that the story—about Lt. Joe Cable's tender romance with Liat, a Polynesian girl—was a bit too much like Madame Butterfly, and they suggested that another story in the collection, "Our Heroine," should provide the main plot. This one was about the unlikely attraction between Nellie Forbush, a naïve Navy nurse from Little Rock, and Emile de Becque, a sophisticated French planter living on a Pacific island. The tales were combined by having Cable and de Becque go on a dangerous mission together behind Japanese lines. Coming just a few years after the war, and featuring several veterans in the cast, the show was enormously resonant with 1949 audiences. But there has not so far been a major Broadway revival. Perhaps because of its daring (for the time) theme of the evils of racial prejudice, it was also the second musical to be awarded the prestigious Pulitzer Prize for Drama. This production was the first of two musicals (the other was *The Sound of Music*) in which Mary Martin, who played Nellie, was seen as a Rodgers and Hammerstein heroine. It also marked the Broadway debut of famed Metropolitan Opera basso, Ezio Pinza, who played de Becque. Mitzi Gaynor and Rossano Brazzi starred in 20th Century-Fox's 1958 film version, also directed by Logan.

SUNSET BOULEVARD

MUSIC: Andrew Lloyd Webber
LYRICS AND BOOK: Don Black and Christopher Hampton
OPENED: 12/7/93, London; 17/11/94, New York

Sunset Boulevard, based on the 1950 Billy Wilder film, provided Broadway and the West End with one of the greatest diva vehicles ever. Dealing with a tortured woman whose advancing age leads to rejection and madness, this musical shows the debilitating aftereffects of Hollywood stardom in all their gothic glory. The show premiered in London in 1993 with Patti LuPone as the former silent screen star Norma Desmond who is desperate to make a comeback (though she loathes that word). After several lawsuits, the Broadway role went to Glenn Close, who had played the show in Los Angeles. Elaine Page and Bettye Buckley also distinguished themselves in the lead role. The story involves a young screenwriter who stumbles into Norma Desmond's life. She falls in love with him, and he accepts her lavish attention. Miss Desmond has a pathetic plan to return to the screen with her own hopelessly overwritten adaptation of Salome. She thrills when the studio invites her to come by. But she's then crushed when she learns they don't want her—they want her vintage car, as an antique prop. Her life and sanity quickly fly apart, with tragic consequences for all. In a song for Miss Desmond's butler (who turns out to be her husband!), her greatest fan cautions Joe that he must show the goddess the ultimate respect because, after all, she was once "The Greatest Star of All."

THE UNSINKABLE MOLLY BROWN

MUSIC AND LYRICS: Meredith Willson
BOOK: Richard Morris
OPENED: 3/11/60, New York

Having made his Broadway bow with *The Music Man*, composer Meredith Willson had a tough act to follow. He chose another rural American subject, real-life feisty Colorado mining millionairess Molly Brown, whose life is also changed in 1912. Determined to leave the poverty of her girlhood far behind, she meets and marries rough-hewn mining wunderkind Leadville Johnny Brown, rises to the top of Denver society, then sets out to conquer Europe. Her odyssey lands her on the *Titanic*, where once again her determination literally to rise above it all stands her in very good stead, and earns her the nickname of the title. Early in the show, when still poor, Johnny declared his love for Molly in "I'll Never Say No."

GASTON

from Walt Disney's *Beauty and the Beast:*
The Broadway Musical

Lyrics by HOWARD ASHMAN
Music by ALAN MENKEN

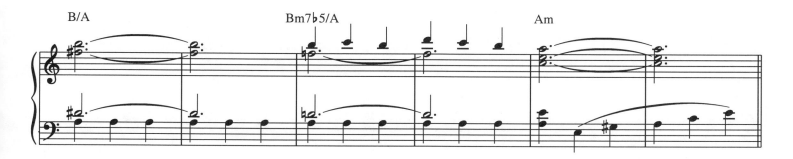

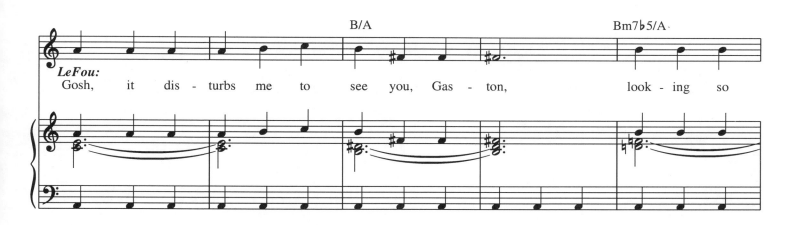

LeFou: Gosh, it dis - turbs me to see you, Gas - ton, look - ing so

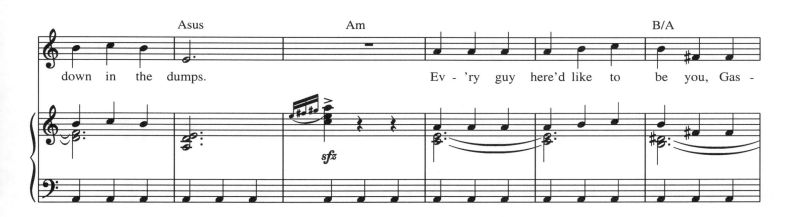

down in the dumps. Ev - 'ry guy here'd like to be you, Gas -

ton, e - ven when tak - ing your lumps. There's

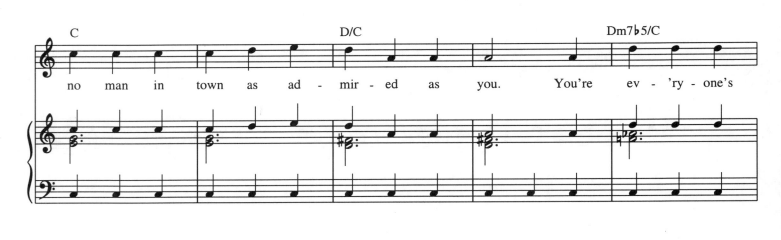

no man in town as ad - mir - ed as you. You're ev - 'ry - one's

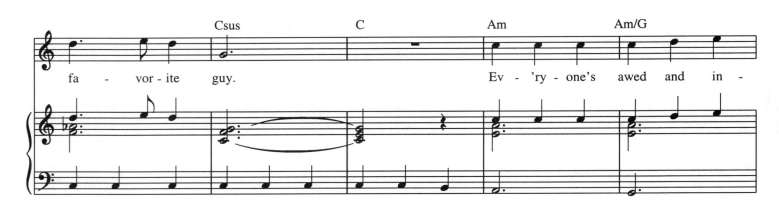

fa - vor - ite guy. Ev - 'ry - one's awed and in -

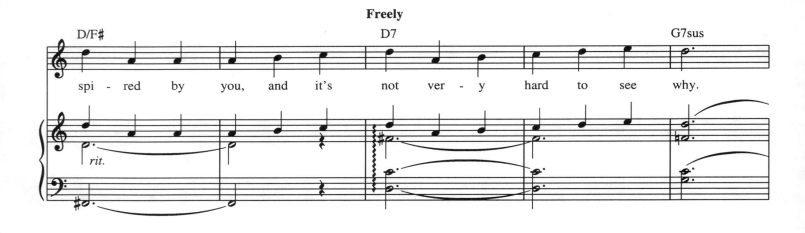

spi - red by you, and it's not ver - y hard to see why.

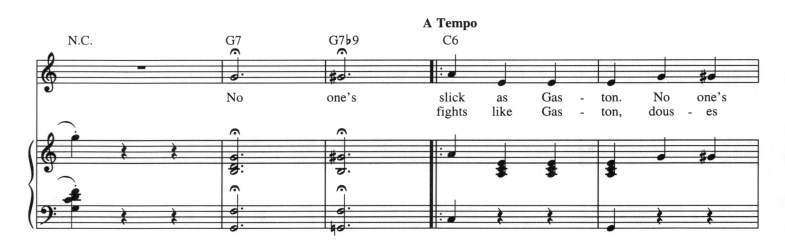

No one's slick as Gas - ton. No one's

fights like Gas - ton, dous - es

Ab7

and they'll tell you whose team they pre - fer to play on. No
right! And ev - 'ry last inch of him cov - ered with hair. No

G7

poco rit.

G7b9 **C6** **G7**

one's been like Gas - ton, a king - pin like Gas - ton No one's got a swell
one hits like Gas - ton, match - es wits like Gas - ton In a spit - ting match,

a tempo

C6 **Am**

cleft in his chin like Gas - ton. As a spec - i - men, yes, he's in -
no - bod - y spits like Gas - ton. He's es - pe - cial - ly good at ex -

D9 **Ab7** **G7** **1** **C**

tim - i - dat - ing! My, what a guy, that Gas - ton! _____
pec - tor - a - ting. Ptoo - ey! Ten points for Gas

18

IF I CAN'T LOVE HER

from Walt Disney's Beauty and the Beast:
The Broadway Musical

Music by ALAN MENKEN
Lyrics by TIM RICE

23

IF I LOVED YOU

from *Carousel*

Words by OSCAR HAMMERSTEIN II
Music by RICHARD RODGERS

Allegretto moderato

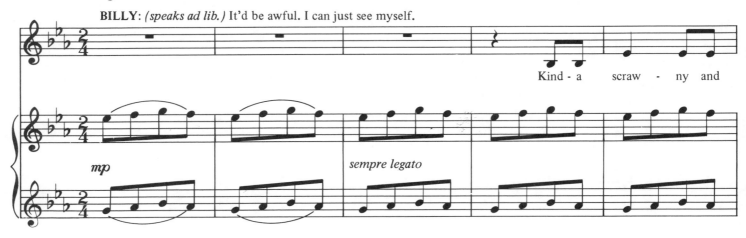

BILLY: *(speaks ad lib.)* It'd be awful. I can just see myself.

Kind-a scraw-ny and

pale, pick-in' at my food And love-sick like an-y oth-er

guy_____ I'd throw a-way my sweat-er And dress up like a

29

All I'd want you to know.

If I loved you, Words would-n't come in an eas-y way

'Round in cir-cles I'd go!

Long-in' to tell you, but a-fraid and shy.

SOLILOQUY
from *Carousel*

Words by OSCAR HAMMERSTEIN II
Music by RICHARD RODGERS

more com-mon sence Than his pud-din' head-ed fa-ther ev-er had._____ I'll

Più mosso

teach him to wras - sle, And dive through a wave, When we go in the morn-in's for our

swim. His moth - er can teach him The way to be - have, But she

won't make a sis - sy out o' him. Not him! Not my boy! Not

36

back._____ Or work up and down The streets of a town With a

whip and a horse and a hack._____ He can haul a scow a-

long a can-al, Run a cow a-round a cor-ral, Or may-be bark for a

car-rou-sel Of course it takes tal-ent to do that well. He

might be a champ of the heav - y-weights, Or a fel - ler that sells you

glue, ___ Or Pres-i-dent of the U - nit - ed States That-'d be al - right,

too. ___

(Speaks ad lib.)

His mother would like that. But he wouldn't be

(Sings)

President unless he wanted to be. Not Bill!

42

fun with a son, But you got to be a fa-ther To a girl!_____

_____ She might-n't be so bad at that,_____ A kid with

rib - bons In her hair!_____ A kind o' neat and pe - tite Lit - tle

(Spoken) I can just hear myself
bragging about her!

tin - type of her moth-er! What a pair!_____

44

She has a few Pink and white young fel-lers of two and three But

my lit-tle girl Gets hun-gry ev-'ry night and she comes home to

Poco più mosso
(Spoken) My little girl, my little girl!

me! I got to get read-y be-

fore she comes! I got to make cer-tain that she Won't be dragged up in slums With a

46

SORRY-GRATEFUL
from *Company*

Words and Music by STEPHEN SONDHEIM

Rubato (♩ = 60)

HARRY:
You're al-ways sor-ry,_ You're al-ways grate-ful,_ You're

Strict rhythm

al-ways wond-'ring_ what might have been._ Then she walks in._ And

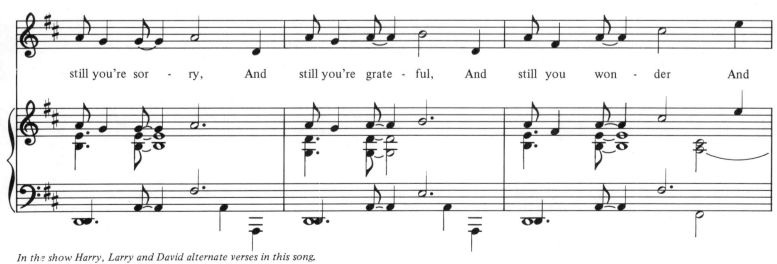

still you're sor-ry, And still you're grate-ful, And still you won-der And

In the show Harry, Larry and David alternate verses in this song.

still you doubt,_ And she goes out._ Ev-'ry-thing's diff-'rent,

Noth-ing's changed,_ On-ly may-be slight-ly re-ar-ranged._ You're

sor-ry — grate-ful, Re-gret-ful — hap-py; Why look for an-swers where

none oc-cur?_ You al-ways are_ what you al-ways were,_ Which has

Strict rhythm

50

nothing to do with, All to do with her._____ You'll

al-ways be__ what you al-ways were,_ Which has noth-ing to do with, All to do with

Strict rhythm

her._____ Noth-ing to do with, All to do with

her._____

ppp

MARRY ME A LITTLE

from *Company*

Music and Lyrics by
STEPHEN SONDHEIM

Allegro appassionata (♩ = 80)

mp legato

mp espress.

Mar-ry me ____ a lit-tle, Love me just ____ e-nough.

Cry, __ but ____ not too of-ten, Play, __ but ____ not too rough.

Keep a ten - der dis - tance, So we'll both ____ be free.

That's the way ____ it ought to be. ____

cresc.

sub. *f*   *mp*

I'm read - y!   Mar - ry   me ____   a lit - tle,

mp

Do it with ____ a will.   Make a few ____ de-mands I'm

a - ble to ____ ful-fill.   Want me more ____ than oth - ers,

54

You can be _____ my best friend. _____

I can be _____ your right arm. _____

We'll go through ___ a fight or two. ____ No

harm, _____ No harm. _____ We'll

Pas-sion - ate _____ as hell, But Al-ways in _____ con-trol.

Want me first _____ and fore - most, Keep me com - pan-y.

That's the way _____ it ought to be. _____

I'm read - y! I'm read - y!

now!

mf legato   *dim.*

p

Oh, how gent - ly we'll talk, _____

p

_____ Oh, how soft - ly we'll tread. _____

_____ All the stings, ___ The ug - ly things ___

We'll keep _____ un - said. _____

We'll build a _____ co -

coon Of love and _____

_____ re - spect. You

prom - ise _____ what - ev - er you like, I'll nev - er col - lect. _____ Right? O - kay, then, I'm read - y!

63

DO I LOVE YOU BECAUSE YOU'RE BEAUTIFUL?

from *Cinderella*

Words by OSCAR HAMMERSTEIN II
Music by RICHARD RODGERS

love - ly to _____ be real - ly true? Do I

want you be-cause you're won - der-ful? _____ Or are you won - der-ful _____ be - cause I

want you? _____ Are you the sweet in - ven-tion of a lov - er's dream,_____

_____ Or are you real - ly as beau - ti - ful as you seem. _____

Largo

THE ROAD YOU DIDN'T TAKE

from *Follies*

Words and Music by STEPHEN SONDHEIM

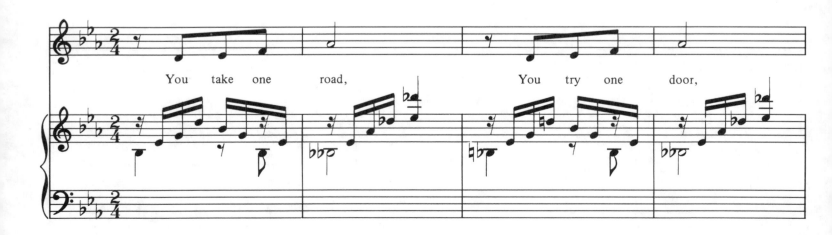

There is - n't time for an - y more.

One's life con - sists of ei - ther / or. One has re -

grets which one for - gets, And as the

years go on, The

road you did-n't take hard-ly comes to mind, Does it? _____ The

door you did-n't try, Where could it have led? _____ The

choice you did-n't make nev-er was de-fined, Was it? _____

Dreams you did-n't dare _____ are dead. Were they ev-er there? _____ Who said? I

don't re - mem - ber, I don't re - mem - ber at

all. _____

The

books I'll nev - er read would - n't change a thing, Would they? _____ The

won't re - mem - ber at all, _____ Not at

all. _____ You yearn for the wom - en,

Long for the mon - ey, En - vy the fa - mous Ben - ja - min Stones.

You take your road, The dec - ades fly,

The yearn-ings fade, the long-ings die. _____ You learn to

bid them all good-bye. _____ And oh, the peace, _____ the bless-ed

poco rit.

peace. _____ At last you come to know; _____

8va - - - - - - - - - -

cresc.

a tempo

The roads you nev-er take go through rock-y

a tempo

MY TIME OF DAY
from *Guys and Dolls*

Words and Music by
FRANK LOESSER

mop _____ And the gro - cer - y clerks are all gone _____ When the

smell __ of the rain - washed pave - ment _____ Comes up clean and fresh and cold _____ And the

street lamp - light _____ fills the gut - ter with gold _____ That's my time of day

My time of day, And you're the on - ly doll I've ev - er want - ed, to share it with me.__

LUCK BE A LADY
from *Guys and Dolls*

Words and Music by
FRANK LOESSER

lush   And yet be-fore this eve-ning is o-ver you might give me the brush__

You might for-get your man-ners, You might re-fuse to

stay   And   so the best that I can do is pray. _____

Luck   be   a   la - dy to - night._

78

Luck let a gen - tle - man see _____

How nice a dame you can be _____

I know the way you've treat - ed oth - er guys ___ you've been with,

Luck be a la - dy with me! _____

A la-dy does-n't leave her es-cort _____ It is-n't fair, _____ it is-n't nice. _____ A la-dy does-n't wan-der all o - ver the room And blow on some oth-er guy's

dice. _____ So let's keep the par - ty po - lite. _

Nev - er get out of my sight _

Stick with me ba - by I'm the

fel - low you came in with. Luck be a la - dy,

84

MORE I CANNOT WISH YOU

from *Guys and Dolls*

By FRANK LOESSER

call-ing cards_ up - on a sil - ver tray _____ But more I can-not wish_ you than to

wish you find your love, ___ Your own true love, this day _____

Stand - ing there _____ Gaz-ing at you _____ Full ___ of the

bloom ___ of youth Stand- ing there _____ Gaz-ing at you ___

With the sheep's eye _____ And the lick-er-ish tooth

Mu - sic I can wish you, mer-ry mu-sic while you're young,—— And wis-dom, when your

hair has turned to gray ———————— But more I can-not wish—— you than to

wish you find your love,——— Your own true love,——— this day———

——— With the sheep's eye And the lick-er-ish tooth And the

strong arms to car-ry you a-way.———

BYE BYE BABY

from *Gentlemen Prefer Blondes*

Words and Music by
LEO ROBIN and JULE STYNE

When they give you the eye. _____ Al - though I
know that you care, _ Won't you write _ and de - clare _ That
though on the loose, _ You are still _ on the square. _
I'll be gloom - y, But send that rain - bow to me

91

Then my shad-ows will fly,_____ Though you'll be

gone for a-while___ I know that I'll be smil-ing With my

1.
ba-by bye and bye. 2. bye,_____ With my

ba-by ___ bye and bye._____

PILATE'S DREAM

from *Jesus Christ Superstar*

Lyrics by TIM RICE
Music by ANDREW LLOYD WEBBER

MCA music publishing

LES POISSONS

from *The Little Mermaid*

Lyrics by HOWARD ASHMAN
Music by ALAN MENKEN

DULCINEA
from *Man of La Mancha*

Words by JOE DARION
Music by MITCH LEIGH

we have been al-ways a - part. Dul - ci - ne - a...

Dul - ci - ne - a... I see heav - en when I

see thee, Dul - ci - ne - a, And thy name is like a

prayer an an - gel whis - pers... Dul - ci - ne - a...

Dul - ci - ne - a! _____ If I reach out to

thee, Do not trem-ble and shrink from the touch of my hand on thy hair, _____

_____ Let my fin - gers but see Thou art warm and a - live, and no

phan-tom to fade in the air. _____ Dul - ci - ne - a...

Dul - ci - ne - a... I have sought thee, sung thee,

dreamed thee, Dul - ci - ne - a! Now I've found thee, and the

world shall know thy glo - ry, Dul - ci - ne - a...

rall.

A tempo

Dul - ci - ne - a!

p

pp

THE IMPOSSIBLE DREAM

from *Man of La Mancha*

Words by JOE DARION
Music by MITCH LEIGH

run _____ where the brave dare not go; _____ To right _____ the un-right-a-ble

wrong, _____ To love, _____ pure and chaste, from a-

far, _____ To try, _____ when your arms are too wear-y, _____ To

reach _____ the un-reach-a-ble star! This is my

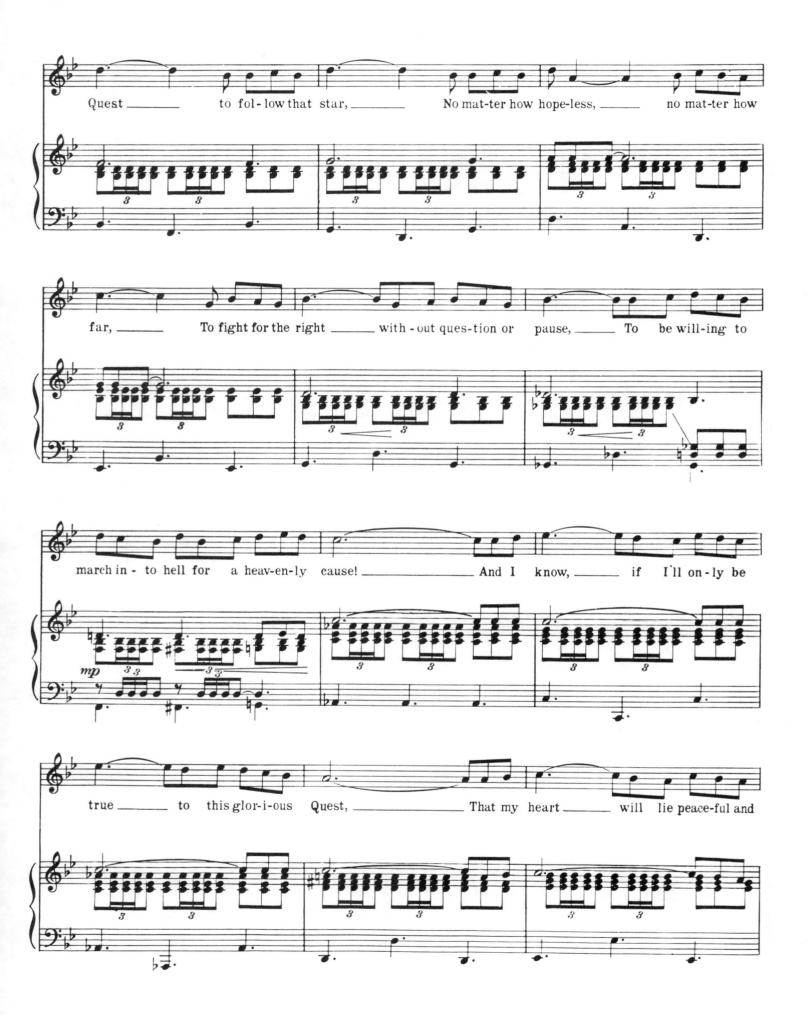

Quest ____ to fol-low that star, ____ No mat-ter how hope-less, ____ no mat-ter how

far, ____ To fight for the right ____ with-out ques-tion or pause, ____ To be will-ing to

march in - to hell for a heav-en-ly cause! ____ And I know, ____ if I'll on-ly be

true ____ to this glor-i-ous Quest, ____ That my heart ____ will lie peace-ful and

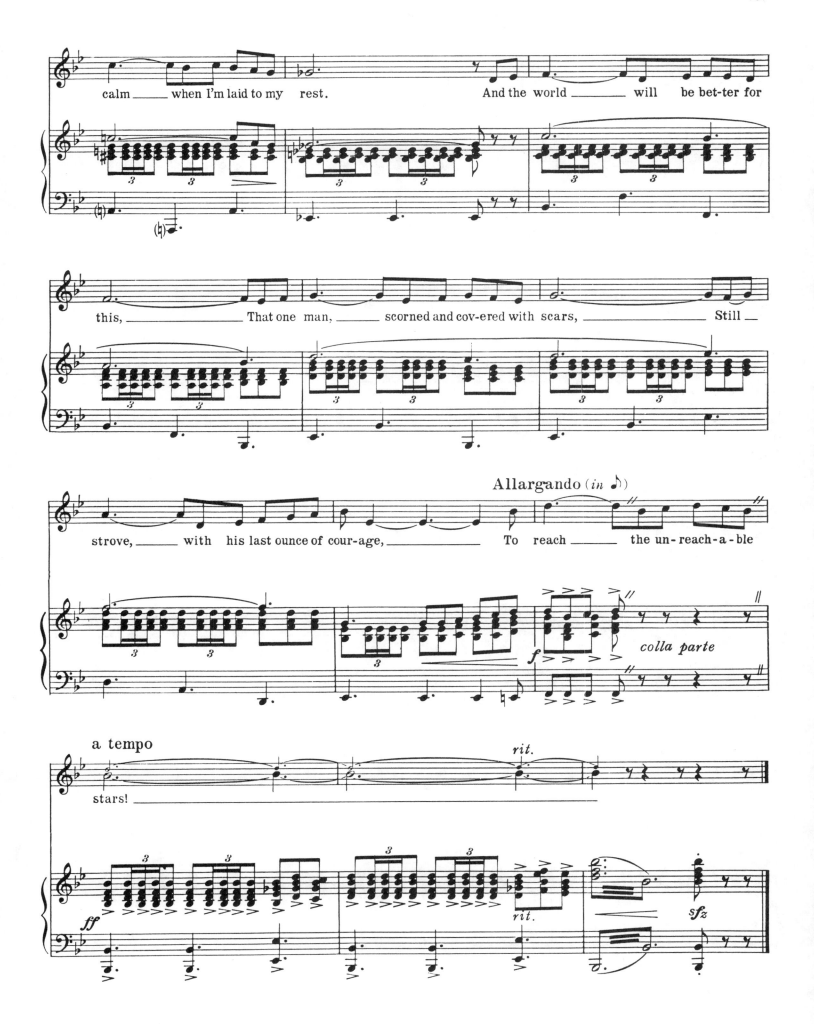

calm _____ when I'm laid to my rest. And the world _____ will be bet-ter for

this, _____ That one man, _____ scorned and cov-ered with scars, _____ Still _____

Allargando (*in* ♪)

colla parte

strove, _____ with his last ounce of cour-age, _____ To reach _____ the un-reach-a-ble

a tempo *rit.*

stars! _____

THE MAN OF LA MANCHA
(I, Don Quixote)
from *Man of La Mancha*

Words by JOE DARION
Music by MITCH LEIGH

In the show this is sung as a duet between Don Quixote and Sancho Panza.

furled Now hurls down his gaunt-let to thee! ____

____ I am I, Don Qui-xo-te, The Lord of La

Man-cha, My des-tin-y calls and I go, ____

____ And the wild winds of for-tune will car-ry me

on - ward, Oh whith - er - so - ev - er they blow.

Whith - er - so - ev - er they blow,

On - ward__ to glo - ry I go!

Hear me, heath - ens__ and wiz - ards and

ser - pents of sin! All your das - tard - ly do - ings are

past, _____ For a ho - ly _____ en - deav - or is

now to _____ be - gin And vir - tue _____ shall

tri - umph at last! _____

I am I, Don Qui xo - te, The Lord of La

Man - cha, My des - tin - y calls and I go, _____

_____ And the wild winds of for - tune will car - ry me

on - ward, Oh whith - er - so - ev - er they blow! _____

JUSTICE WILL BE DONE
from *Martin Guerre*

Music by CLAUDE-MICHEL SCHÖNBERG
Lyrics by ALAIN BOUBLIL and STEPHEN CLARK

fight - ing   for   our   hearts.   Let us   join to - ge - ther,   stand up   one by one.

In   the   name   of   Je - sus   just - ice   will   be

done!

STARS
from *Les Misérables*

Lyrics by HERBERT KRETZMER
and ALAIN BOUBLIL
Music by CLAUDE-MICHEL SCHÖNBERG

120

aim.   And each in your sea - son re - turns and   re - turns   and is al - ways the

same.   And if you fall   as Lu - ci - fer fell,   you

fall _____ in flame!   And so it has been, and so it is writ - ten   on the

door - ways to par - a - dise, _____ that those who fal - ter and those who fall _____ must

EMPTY CHAIRS AT EMPTY TABLES

(The Café Song)
from *Les Misérables*

Lyrics by HERBERT KRETZMER
and ALAIN BOUBLIL
Music by CLAUDE-MICHEL SCHÖNBERG

126

LEANING ON A LAMP-POST

from *Me and My Girl*

Words and Music by
NOEL GAY

Lean - ing on a lamp, May-be you think I look a tramp, Or you may

think I'm hang-ing 'round to steal a car. But

no, I'm not a crook, And if you think that's what I look, I'll tell you

don't know if she'll get a- way,_ She does-n't al - ways get a- way,_ But an - y-way   I know that she'll

try.   Oh   me,   Oh   my,   I

hope   the lit - tle la - dy comes   by.   There's   no   oth - er girl   I   could

wait   for,   But   this   one   I'd break   an - y date for,   I

won't have to ask what she's late for, She would-n't leave me flat, She's not a

girl like that. She's ab - so-lute - ly won - der-ful and mar - vel-ous and beau - ti-ful, And

an - y-one can un - der-stand why I'm lean - ing on a lamp-post at the

cor - ner of the street, In case a cer - tain lit - tle la - dy comes by.

ab - so - lute - ly won - der - ful and mar - vel - ous and beau - ti - ful, __ And an - y - one __ can un - der - stand

why I'm lean - ing on a lamp - post at the cor - ner of the street, In case a

cer - tain lit - tle la - dy comes by. ____

Grazioso

opt. just play top note

JOEY, JOEY, JOEY

from *The Most Happy Fella*

By FRANK LOESSER

Sings to me _____ When the bunk I've been bunk-in' in

Cl.,Cello

Strgs. pizz.

_____ gets to feel-in' too soft and co-zy, _____ When the

grub they've been cook-in' me _____ gets to tast-in' too good, _____

Vls.,Fl.

_____ When I've had all I want of the la-dies in the neigh-bor-

Vls.

And it's time to go,_____ time to go!_____

Jo - ey,_____ Jo - ey, Joe!_____

GUIDO'S SONG

from *Nine*

Lyrics and Music by
MAURY YESTON

prob - lem ___ es - pe - cial - ly when my bod - y's clear - ing

for - ty as my mind is near - ing ten. I can hard - ly stay

up, and I can't get to sleep, and I don't want to

wake to - mor - row morn - ing at the bot - tom of some heap, but why

take it so se - ri - ous - ly? Af - ter

all there's noth-ing at stake here— on - ly me! I want to be

young, and I want to be old. I would like to be

wise be - fore my time, and yet, be fool - ish and brash and bold— I would like the

144

have to be-lieve in God, and you know I mean it with all of my

heart— it's the end of some-thing im-por-tant does-n't

start... I want to be young, but I have to be

old. What I want is a tale of sound and fu-ry that some

LONELY ROOM

from *Oklahoma!*

Words by OSCAR HAMMERSTEIN II
Music by RICHARD RODGERS

slants down a beam 'crost my bed, Then the

shad-der of a tree starts a-danc-in' on the wall And a

dream starts a-danc-in' in my head. And

all the things that I wish fer Turn

152

own soft arms keep me warm. And her

long, yel-ler hair falls a-crost my face, Jist like the rain in a storm!

Moderato

The floor creaks, The door squeaks, And the

cross hands

mouse starts a - nib-blin' on the broom. And the sun flicks my eyes, It was

OH, WHAT A BEAUTIFUL MORNIN'

from *Oklahoma!*

Words by OSCAR HAMMERSTEIN II
Music by RICHARD RODGERS

156

in' Ev-'ry-thin's go-in' my way._____

All the cat-tle are stand-in' like stat-ues,_____ All the

cat-tle are stand-in' like stat-ues,_____ They

159

sounds of the earth are like mu - sic, _____ The

breeze is so bus - y, it don't miss a tree, And an

ol' weep - in' wil - ler is laugh - in' at me.

Oh, what a beau - ti - ful morn - in',

THE SURREY WITH THE FRINGE ON TOP

from *Oklahoma!*

Lyrics by OSCAR HAMMERSTEIN II
Music by RICHARD RODGERS

164

166

Brightly

I would say the fringe was made of silk ____

Would-n't have no oth-er kind but silk ____

It has real-ly got a team of snow-white hors - es

One's like snow, the oth-er's more like milk. ____

poco rit

+ Hns. Guit.
mod.to marcato

*The lyrics at these two spots have been altered just slightly for a solo singer version. The top line of the page, sung by Aunt Eller in the show, is "Would you say the fringe was made of silk?" The third line, sung by Laurey in the show, is "Has it really got a team of snow-white horses?"

Tempo giusto

All the world -'ll fly in a flur - ry When I take you

out in the sur-rey When I take you out in the sur-rey with the

fringe on top! When we hit that

road, hell fer leath-er, Cats and dogs -'ll dance in the heath-er

Birds and frogs-'ll sing all to-geth-er and the toads will hop! The wind-'ll whis-tle as we rat-tle a-long, The cows-'ll moo in the clov-er, The riv-er will rip-ple out a whis-pered song, and whis-per it o-ver and o-ver:

Con sentimento (*slowly*)

I can see the stars git-tin' blur-ry When we ride back home in the sur-rey, Rid-in' slow-ly home in the sur-rey with the fringe on top. I can feel the day git-tin' old-er, Feel a sleep-y - head near my shoul-der,

172

Hush! You bird, my ba-by's a-sleep-in' May-be got a
Stgs.
(Cel.)
(gradually slower to the end)
dream worth a-keep-in' Whoa! you team, and jist keep a-creep-in' at a
slow clip clop. Don't you hur-ry with the sur-rey with the
fringe on the top.
pp rit. e dim.
+ Hp.

IT'S HARD TO SPEAK MY HEART

from *Parade*

Music and Lyrics by
JASON ROBERT BROWN

With a sense of stillness (♩ = 69)

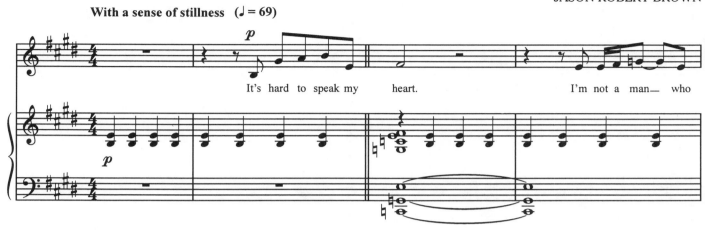

It's hard to speak my heart. I'm not a man who

bares his soul. I let the mo-ment pass me by; I stay where I am

in con-trol. I hide be-hind my work, safe and sure of what to

LONELY TOWN

from *On the Town*

Words by BETTY COMDEN
and ADOLPH GREEN
Music by LEONARD BERNSTEIN

182

ILONA

from *She Loves Me*

Lyrics by SHELDON HARNICK
Music by JERRY BOCK

How I en - vy you each eve - 'ning, when work is through, For

Rubato

I have on - ly me to be with while you have you. With -

A Tempo

out you, _____ Il - o - na, _____ How

cold my lone - ly life has grown. _____ Are you

ie. _____ Mis - tle - toe, I long for some - one,

please tell me who. Like some di - vine di - vin - ing rod, it

points straight to you. **Rubato** Re - mem - ber, _____ **A Tempo** Il -

* (kiss)

o - na. _____ The sun - ny nights we knew be -

* Kodaly kisses the air, or blows a kiss.

OL' MAN RIVER

from *Show Boat*

Words by OSCAR HAMMERSTEIN II
Music by JEROME KERN

*Joe is accompanied by chorus in this scene in the show.

Tote dat barge! Lift dat bale! Git a lit-tle drunk An' you land in jail.

colla voce

I git wear-y An' sick of try-in', I'm tired of liv-in' An' skeered of dy-in'; But

ol' man riv-er, He jes' keeps rol-lin' a - long!

Col-ored folks work on de Mis - sis - sip - pi, Col-ored folks work while de

194

You an' me, we sweat an' strain, Bod-y all ach-in' an' wracked wid' pain.

Tote dat barge! An' lift dat bale! Git a lit-tle drunk an' you land in jail.

poco a poco cresc.

I git wear-y An' sick of try-in', I'm tired of liv-in' An' skeered of dy-in'; But

(full)
poco a poco cresc.

ol' man riv-er He jes' keeps rol-lin' a - long!

8va

YOU SHOULD BE LOVED

from *Side Show*

Words by BILL RUSSELL
Music by HENRY KRIEGER

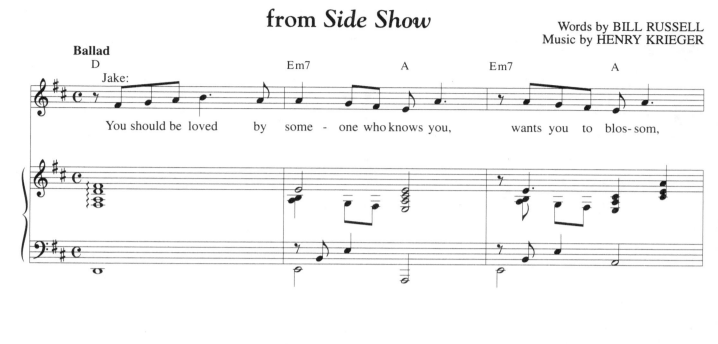

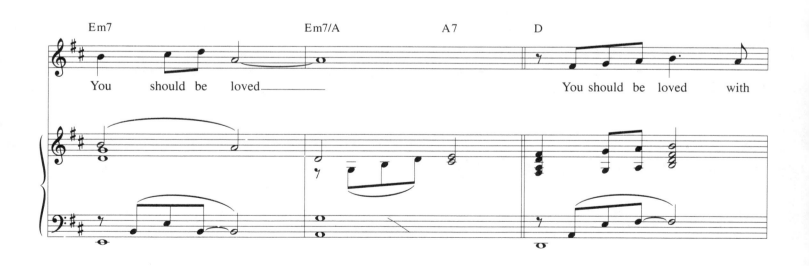

199

SOME ENCHANTED EVENING

from *South Pacific*

Words by OSCAR HAMMERSTEIN II
Music by RICHARD RODGERS

THIS NEARLY WAS MINE

from *South Pacific*

Words by OSCAR HAMMERSTEIN II
Music by RICHARD RODGERS

Tempo di Waltz espressivo

EMILE:

One   dream in my   heart_____   One

par-a-dise _____ This near-ly was mine. _____

Close to my heart she came _____ On-ly to fly a-

way _____ On-ly to fly as day flies from

moon-light. _____ Now, now I'm a-lone _____

*Repeat can be started here.

210

THE GREATEST STAR OF THEM ALL

from *Sunset Boulevard*

Music by ANDREW LLOYD WEBBER
Lyrics by DON BLACK and CHRISTOPHER HAMPTON,
with contributions by AMY POWERS

213

I'LL NEVER SAY NO
from *The Unsinkable Molly Brown*

Words and Music by
MEREDITH WILLSON

JOHNNY:

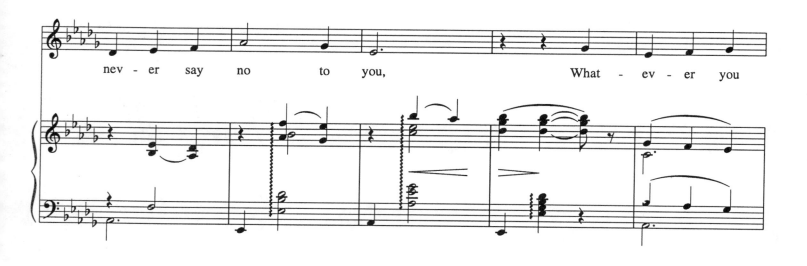

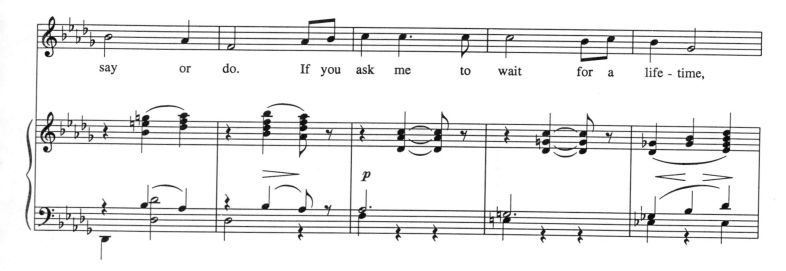

But I'll nev - er say no.

cresc. ed accel. poco a poco

Faster *(Surging forward with impassioned drive)*

I'll smile when you say: "Be